Motorcycles: How They Work

About the Book

Knowing how a motorcycle works is possibly second in importance to knowing how it responds, how it handles, and how it will bounce or swerve on rough terrain. All those "hows" are in these pages, plus how to select a motorcycle when you come of age, and how to ride it.

Motorcycles
How They Work

by Charles Yerkow

G. P. Putnam's Sons   New York

To

Frank Sloan

Fourth Impression
SBN GB 399-60477-4
Copyright © 1971 by Charles Yerkow
All rights reserved. Published simultaneously in
Canada by Longmans Canada Limited, Toronto.
Library of Congress Catalog Card Number: 79-146104
PRINTED IN THE UNITED STATES OF AMERICA
12216

Contents

Foreword **7**
1. Motorcycles and Adventures **9**
2. The Motorcycle Engine **20**
3. The Clutch and Gear System **42**
4. The Frame and the Suspension **53**
5. Switches, Controls, and Indicators **62**
6. Important Maintenance **68**
7. How to Ride a Motorcycle **72**
8. Selecting a Motorcycle **80**
Index **94**

The How It Works Books

AIRPLANES: How They Work
by Kenton D. McFarland

AUTOMOBILES: How They Work
by Charles Yerkow

COMMUNICATIONS SATELLITES: How They Work
by Alvin Lukashok

THE ELECTRONIC BRAIN: How It Works
by Joseph J. Cook

LASERS: How They Work
by Charles H. Wacker, Jr.

MOTORCYCLES: How They Work
by Charles Yerkow

PARACHUTES: How They Work
by Eloise Engle

RADAR: How It Works
by Raymond F. Jones

THE TELEPHONE: How It Works
by Jerome J. O'Connor

WEATHER INSTRUMENTS: How They Work
by Irwin Stambler

Foreword

The purpose of this book is to inform you about the many parts that make up a motorcycle—from the frame and the suspension on up to the engine and the techniques of how to select a bike and how to ride it.

Throughout the book different illustrations are used to explain how certain parts of a machine work, but the sequence of the illustrations is not necessarily related to the same motorcycle. Also, in order to provide meaningful comparisons in performance capabilities of motorcycles, the mention of speeds, engine power and types, mileages, and other technical information is in no way intended to imply that other motorcycles are not able to perform as well or even better. The enthusiast who is interested solely in the competition type of machine will have to search out other sources for technical information, as those motorcycles are highly specialized.

The writer is grateful to all who supplied information

and illustrative material for this book: Ted Burke, American Jawa; Emmett Moore, Eastern Kawasaki Motorcycle Corporation; Lawrence Wise and Joseph Rottigni, Cosmopolitan Motors (Benelli, MV Agusta); Richard Kahn, Butler & Smith (BMW); American Honda Motor Company; Harley-Davidson Motor Company; Berliner Motor Corporation (Ducati, Moto-Guzzi, Norton); U.S. Suzuki Motor Corporation; and BSA/Triumph East. Special thanks also to David C. Cooke, Tom Washburn, Phil Smith, Don Whyte, V. Jarolim, Tom MacPherson, and the staff at G. P. Putnam.

CHARLES YERKOW

1

Motorcycles and Adventures

When the first bicycle was invented in 1790, hardly anyone imagined that someday a small engine would be mounted in a similar frame and used to propel the rider at speeds of 50, 90, and even 125 miles per hour. Historically, the very first attempts to motorize the bicycle were made in Winthrop, Massachusetts, in 1866 when W. W. Austin fitted a steam engine between two wheels. The experiment did not prove practical, and the invention of the motorcycle had to wait until 1885 when Gottlieb Daimler in Germany mounted a regular gasoline engine into a robust frame. This experiment was successful, and so the first true motorcycle was born.

The first practical motorcycle in the United States was created by Oscar Hedstrom in 1901. He designed a lightweight single-cylinder machine which performed quite well, and on the basis of its performance the first two-cylinder

This 1915 Pope is in excellent condition and still running. Pushrods and overhead valves, unusual rear spring suspension, full footboards, and magneto behind back cylinder are clearly visible.

(Courtesy of Emmett Moore)

motorcycle was built and unveiled in 1905—to be the forerunner of the famous line of Indian "Scout" and "Chief" motorcycles.

It is of historical interest that as early as 1902 riders were staging races on short dirt tracks, and the natural outcome of these races was a demand for better-performing machines. Thus manufacturers sought ways to improve engines, frames, gearboxes, brakes, and every other part of the machines that were to be used either for transportation or for racing.

For a while certain famous motorcycle names flourished in America, among them Arrow, Cleveland, Excelsior, Henderson, Merkel, and Pope, but then the economic Depression of 1930 caused a drastic reduction in all motorcycle manufacturing. Indian and Harley-Davidson continued for many years afterward, but the only one to survive

Motorcycles are used for transportation and for fun; Tom Washburn and his ten-year-old son Tommy demonstrate how to handle machines for fun. *(Author)*

to the present was Harley-Davidson, with its American-made heavyweight machines and a line of lightweight models made in Italy.

Today the development of efficient, high-performance motorcycles must be credited to European and Japanese manufacturers. The following brief list indicates many known names and the country of origin:

    From Czechoslovakia—Jawa and CZ
        (also distribute Soviet Union made M-1263)
    From England—BSA, Triumph, Matchless, Norton, Royal Enfield
    From Germany—BMW (Bavarian Motor Works)
    From Italy—Benelli, Ducati, Moto-Guzzi, MV Agusta, Parilla
    From Japan—Honda, Kawasaki, Suzuki, Yamaha
    From Spain—Bultaco, Montesa
    From Sweden—Husqvarna

Each manufacturer designs and produces motorcycles in every category, from lightweight types for fun riding to the types used in racing, and on up to the finest for street and open-country touring. Regardless of the size of the machine and the power of its engine, all riders agree about one factor, and that is that the motorcycle provides a thrill—the challenge of being in control of a lively engine in a machine that responds instantly to the slightest lean of the body or touch of lever and throttle. An airline pilot whose hobby is motorcycling said, "I get a bigger thrill out of my bike than from flying a big jet."

Another rider, who likes to race and does his own tuning and repairing, put it this way, "The whole machine is in my mind from the moment I start the engine and shift into gear. I visualize the shafts turning, the clutch plates grab-

During one part of his adventure-packed ride from Alaska to South America, motorcycling enthusiast Danny Liska had to resort to a canoe to get his BMW across a river. (BMW—*Butler & Smith*)

bing, the gears meshing—I can see everything exactly as it's happening. And when the tire bites into the dirt and I surge forward, well, all the money in the world can't buy that feeling of power."

Other enthusiasts, from students to technicians and business executives, express themselves differently. Danny Liska of Niobrara, Nebraska, for example, made a fabulous

A powerful Kawasaki in a hard lean during a race. Note the relaxed left hand on the handlebar and the perfect body position of the rider.
(Eastern Kawasaki Motorcycle Corporation)

adventure-packed run on a BMW from Alaska down through the United States, Central America, and down to the very southern tip of South America—thousands and thousands of miles of riding over every conceivable kind of road and jungle path, across deserts and mountains, in scorching heat and in freezing cold.

Other riders are inclined toward breaking records, so in

when they landed behind enemy lines. These machines, now marketed for public use, are light in weight, easy and safe to control, and will travel over virtually any terrain. Many enterprising people have built their minicycles around lawn-mower engines, a set of wheels, and a homemade frame; others rely on do-it-yourself kits; and some simply purchase the machine in a ready-to-go state.

Motorized bicycles, scooters, and full-scale motorcycles are used throughout the world. Nearly 2,000,000 licensed motorcycle riders are enjoying their machines in the United States alone. The prices for motorcycles range from a few hundred dollars to several thousand. Some machines will cover 60 miles on a gallon of gasoline, others will do 100 miles and even more. One so-called lightweight machine may weigh 100 pounds, but another may weigh 300 pounds. In short, there are all kinds of motorcycles to suit everybody's requirement.

To inform the enthusiasts of trends, new models, new developments, race records, and other matters related to the sport, an impressive group of monthly magazines are available at newsstands. Clubs are also formed throughout the country which provide their members with enjoyable camping trips, technical discussions, and social activities. Needless to say, there are many different types of clubs, and each interested rider must locate the group that appeals to his own character and personal values.

One unfortunate opinion seems to prevail about motorcycles and riders—that the machines are not safe and that the riders are a rough crowd. While it is true that a motorcycle rider is exposed more readily to a spill or crash than the driver of a car (and we have, currently, some 50,000

1	Front fork	14	Petcock	27	Rear foot rest
2	Front fender	15	Tool box	28	Stand
3	Headlamp	16	Strap	29	Kickstart
4	Switch key	17	Seat	30	Foot rest
5	Clutch lever	18	Rear light	31	Brake pedal
6	Dimmer switch	19	Rear fender	32	Oil drain plug
7	Damper	20	Shock absorber	33	Clutch adjuster
8	Handlebar	21	Chain guard	34	Frame
9	Front brake lever	22	Rear wheel	35	Horn
10	Throttle control	23	Rear hub	36	Front wheel
11	Gas cap	24	Chain	37	Front hub
12	Carburetor	25	Chain adjuster		
13	Gastank	26	Rear fork		

This drawing shows the main parts of a motorcycle. The foot-operated gearshift lever on the right side is not visible in this view of a Benelli.

(Cosmopolitan Motors)

people killed yearly in automobiles!), a motorcycle is far more maneuverable than any car and with care and experience a motorcycle rider learns how to avoid dangerous traffic situations.

As for motorcycle riders being rough—if a person is inclined to be rough or a bully, the fault lies within his character rather than his motorcycle. He would be the same if he rode a horse or drove a car or merely walked.

2

The Motorcycle Engine

In 1885 Gottlieb Daimler fitted a rather large engine into the frame of what was to be the first practical motorcycle; in contrast, the engine used by Oscar Hedstrom in 1901 was small, and its single cylinder produced a mere 2.5 horsepower.

The modern motorcycle engine may deliver anywhere from around 5 horsepower on up to 60 horsepower and more, depending on the size of its cylinders. Minibike engines average 2.5 to 5 horsepower, while engines in scooters may be of this or higher power.

The performance of a motorcycle depends on the power output of its engine. While this power is important, other factors must also be considered, such as the size of gears used in the transmission, size of wheels, type of tires, weight of the machine, and other items.

Currently, the popular motorcycle engines are of the

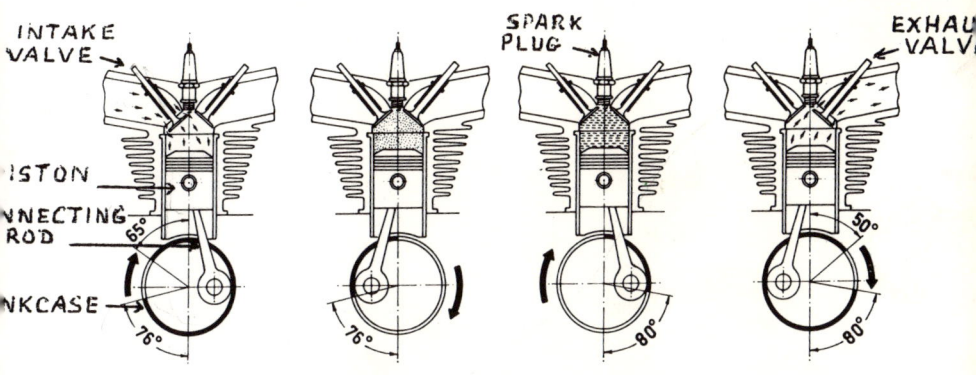

Sequence of a four-stroke engine: intake stroke, compression stroke, power stroke, and exhaust stroke. (*Ducati—Berliner Motor Corporation*)

two-stroke type or the four-stroke type. In the first, the piston inside the cylinder moves up and down twice for every power stroke, while in the second the piston moves four times to accomplish the same task. The job is to turn the crankshaft, which is inside the crankcase. The turning force of this shaft is called torque, and is applied through a set of three, four, five, and even six gears to the main chain, which then turns the rear wheel sprocket. Between the crankshaft and the gears a coupling device, called a clutch, is used to apply engine torque smoothly to the gears.

The manner in which the crankshaft is turned is very simple. An airtight cylinder, attached to the upper part of the crankcase, contains the piston. This piston is joined by a connecting rod to the arm of the crankshaft. As the piston moves up and down inside the cylinder, the crankshaft turns. Because the piston and cylinder must act like a pump, the piston is fitted with expandable steel rings to assure a tight fit around the wall of the cylinder.

As the engine operates with a fuel mixture, cylinders

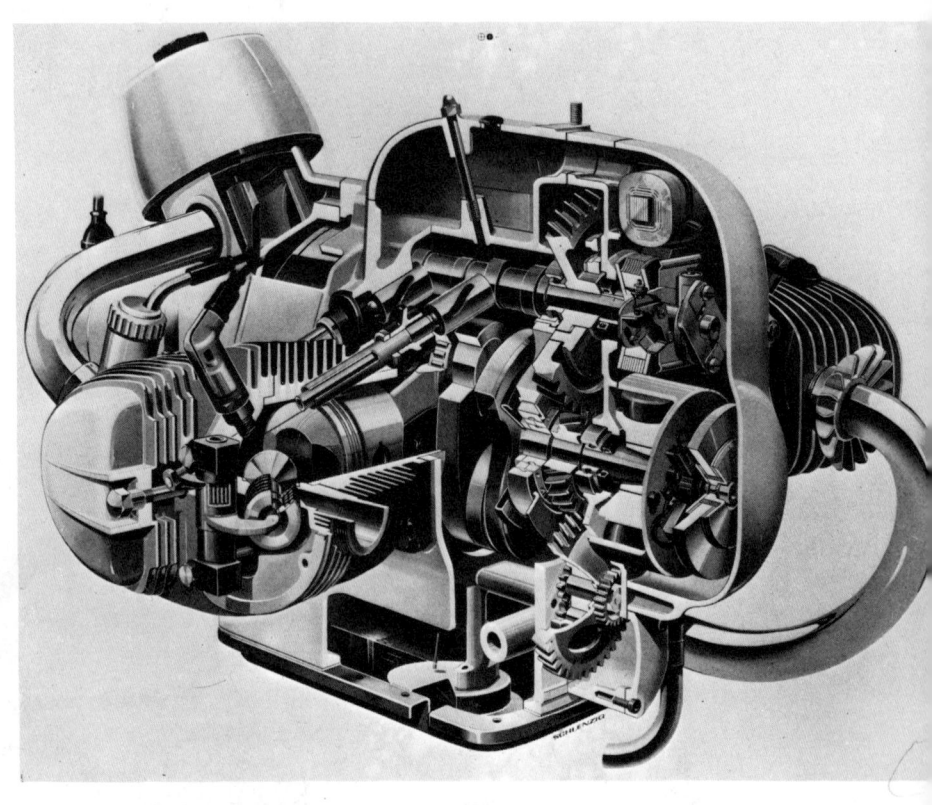

The two cylinders of a four-stroke BMW motorcycle engine are opposed, each with its piston, connecting rod, pushrods, and valve gear.
(BMW—Butler & Smith)

must have a way of letting this mixture into the combustion chamber, and for this purpose valves on four-stroke engines open and close the ports through which the mixture is drawn in and then forced out. On two-stroke engines,

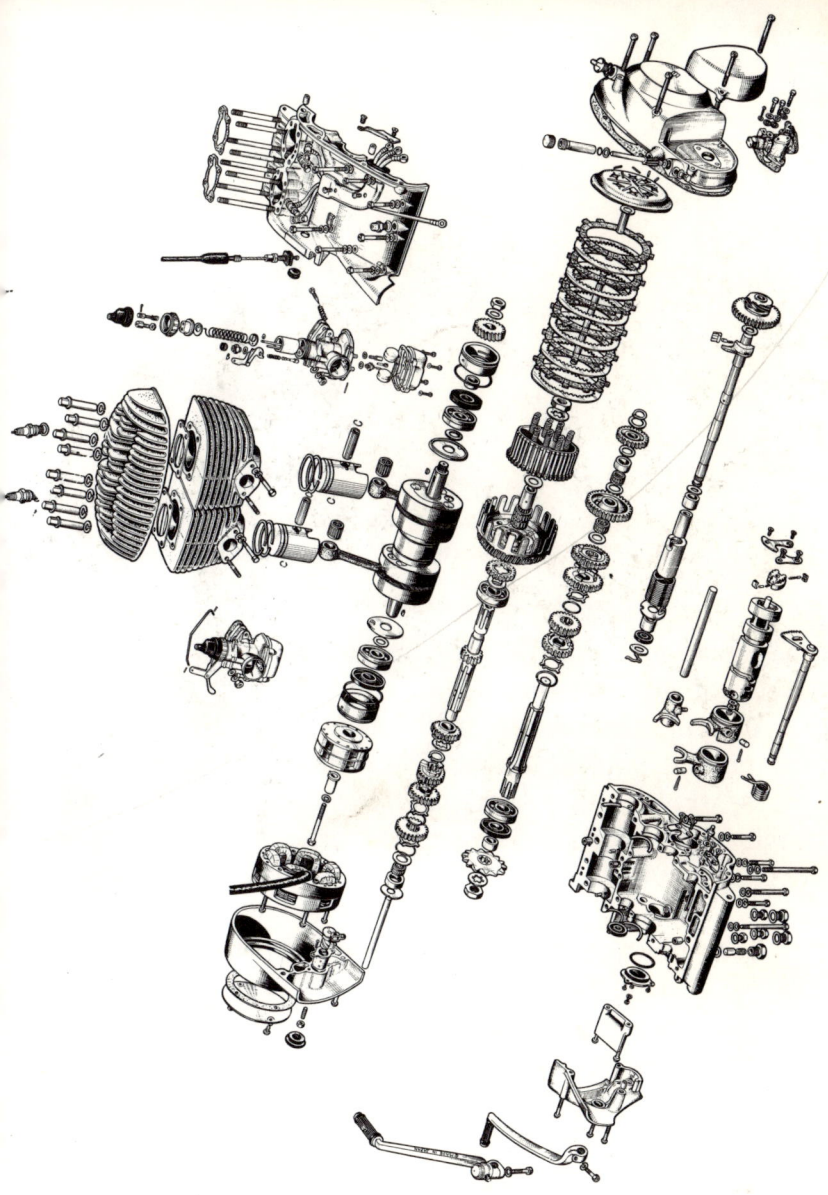

This detailed exploded view of a two-cylinder two-stroke Suzuki T200 engine provides a clear study of all components.
(*U.S. Suzuki Motor Corporation*)

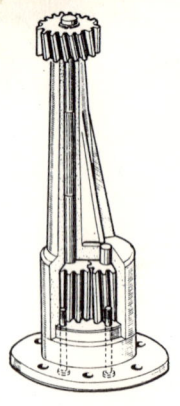

Oil pump

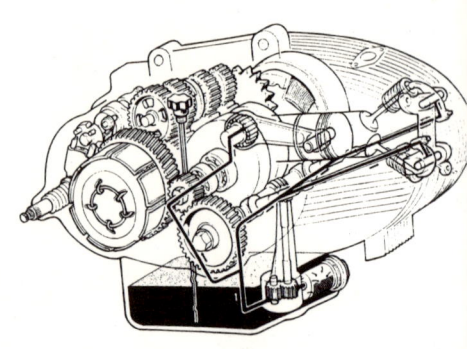

View of oil circulation

The gear-driven oil pump feeds lubricating oil under pressure to the main parts and areas of the four-stroke Benelli engine. (*Cosmopolitan Motors*)

the intake and exhaust ports are uncovered by the piston itself, which means that valves are not used.

After the fuel mixture is drawn into the cylinder and is compressed into the combustion chamber, it is ignited by the sparkplug. The operating sequence of a four-stroke engine (sometimes called the Otto cycle, after the German engineer and inventor August Otto, 1876) is as follows:

1. During the intake stroke, as the piston moves downward, the intake valve opens and the exhaust valve is kept closed. Thus, working inside the airtight cylinder, the movement of the piston creates a vacuum, and this vacuum pulls the fuel mixture of gasoline and air, in the form of a vapor, into the cylinder. As the piston reaches the end of its downward stroke, the intake valve closes. The piston is then at bottom dead center (BDC).
2. The piston now begins its upward stroke, the

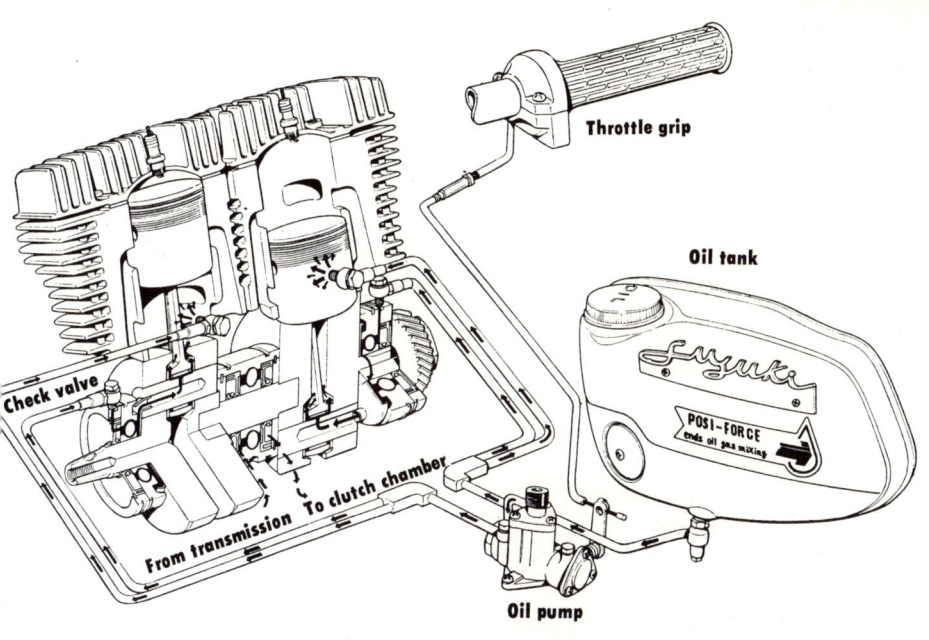

Mixing of gasoline and oil in two-stroke engines has been eliminated by the development of automatic oil injection systems, as shown in this supply, control, and flow diagram. (*U.S. Suzuki Motor Corporation*)

compression stroke, to compress the fuel mixture into the combustion chamber. Both valves are closed at this stage. The interior of the cylinder is of a certain size; thus, if the mixture is compressed into one-seventh part of the cylinder's capacity, the engine is said to have a compression ratio of 7 to 1; if compressed into one-tenth the area, the ratio is 10 to 1. Normally, the higher the ratio, the more powerful the engine.
3. As the piston approaches the top of its upward compression stroke, the sparkplug sets off a spark.

The Ducati 350/450 Desmo engine employs an overhead cam. Note the shaft and valve rocker enclosure at the side of the cylinder, with the attached carburetor, gearshift lever, and kick starter on the far side.
(Berliner Motor Corporation)

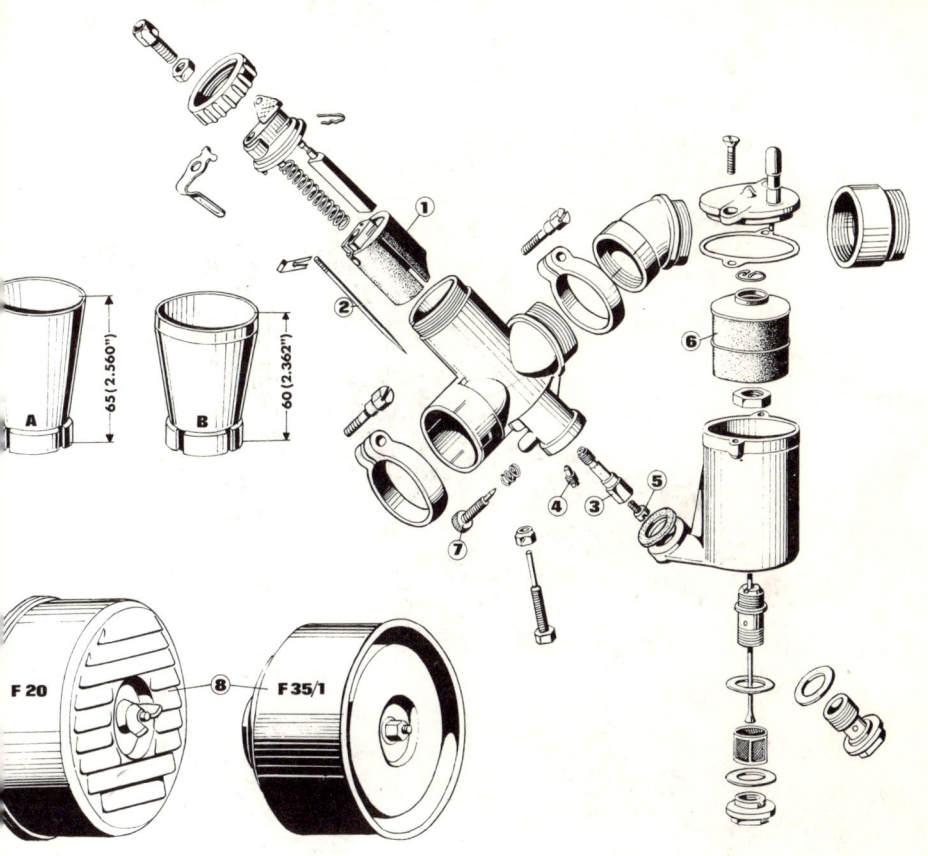

Exploded view of a Dell'Orto carburetor used on Ducati, Benelli, MV Agusta shows: (1) throttle slide, (2) throttle needle, (3) needle jet, (4) idle jet, (5) main jet, (6) float, (7) pilot air idle screw, and (8) air cleaner. Sometimes air horns (A and B) are used instead of air cleaners.

(*Cosmopolitan Motors*)

The fuel mixture is ignited, and the explosion inside the cylinder pushes the piston downward into its power stroke. The spark occurs a few degrees before the piston reaches its top dead center (TDC) position, and is called an advanced

27

spark; if it occurs after this position it is called a retarded spark.

4. As the piston reaches the bottom of its power stroke and starts upward again, the exhaust valve opens and the piston pushes the burned gas out of the cylinder. At the top of this exhaust stroke the exhaust valve closes, the intake valve opens, and the piston starts downward again for the next sequence of intake, compression, power, and exhaust strokes.

These strokes of the piston turn the crankshaft, and the same sequence of operation takes place regardless of the number of cylinders and their arrangement on or around the crankcase. The engine may be a single-cylinder type, called a one-lunger and also nicknamed the "thumper" because of the thumping sound of its exhaust. Other engines use two, three, and four cylinders, which may be set upright side-by-side, or in the case of twins flatly opposite each other, or like a V facing forward or sideways.

The power output of an engine depends largely on the size of the cylinders and the compression ratio. The size is calculated in capacity; in other words, the inside area of the cylinders, measuring the stroke and the width or bore. This area is called the cubic-inch displacement; nearly all manufacturers use the European metric system when stating the size of the engine, and so a 45-cubic-inch engine is a 750-cubic-centimeter (cc) engine. An engine of 750 cc is more powerful than one of 350 cc. However, many factors besides the cylinder capacity affect the performance of the motorcycle, meaning that two identical size 250 cc engines in the same weight machine may perform differently. This performance difference is due to gearing and other factors.

The two-stroke engine sequence is simple in one way and yet complex in another way. This type of engine, patented in 1881 by Sir Dugald Clerk, British engineer and inventor, does not use valves to open and close the cylinder. Instead, this system employs ports or openings in the cylinder wall itself. As the piston moves up and down inside the cylinder, these ports are covered and uncovered in a simple sequence for the intake and exhaust strokes, but are closed by the piston during the compression and power strokes. There is a third port, called the transfer or bypass port, which is also covered and uncovered by the piston during operation.

Currently, the two-stroke rotary disk type engine is popular. Here one port is located at the side of the crankcase instead of in the cylinder wall, and it performs the same functions as the ports on the conventional two-stroke type; the rotating disk is part of the crankshaft and acts to close and open the port as required.

The operating sequence of the conventional two-stroke engine is as follows:
1. Partial compression of the fuel mixture takes place in the crankcase as the piston starts downward in its power stroke, after combustion has taken place. The inlet port is covered (closed). Near the bottom of this stroke the exhaust port is uncovered and the burned gas forced out of the cylinder, then the transfer port is uncovered

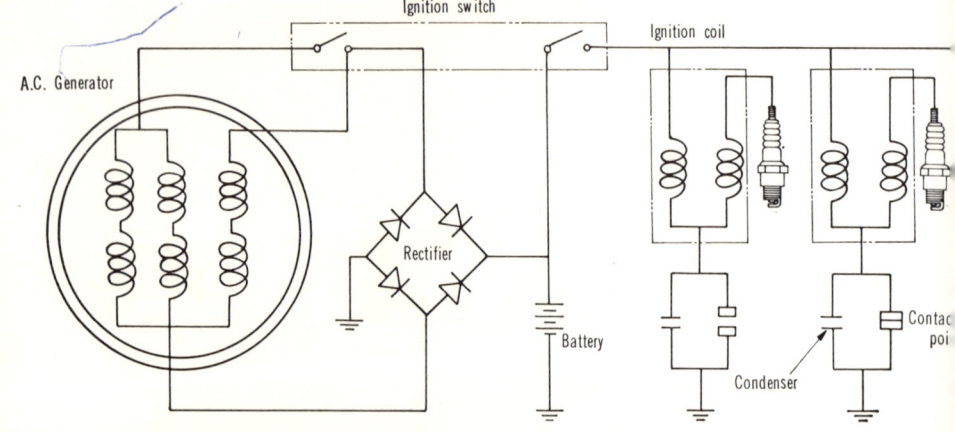

Typical a.c. generator ignition wiring diagram, using six-pole rotating magnet and six-coil stator, with rectifier which alters the a.c. current to d.c. for battery charging. (*U.S. Suzuki*)

and the partially compressed fuel mixture (in this case gasoline, oil, and air) enters the cylinder.

2. As the piston starts upward to compress the fuel mixture, the transfer port is covered first, and then the exhaust port. The piston continues to compress the mixture, but at the same time creates a vacuum within the crankcase and a new fuel mixture rushes into the crankcase through the inlet port. This completes the intake stroke. At this point the piston uncovers the transfer port. The spark ignites the compressed mixture, and the explosion sends the piston down into the power stroke.

The two-stroke engine does not require valves, pushrods, rockers, or oil pump, all of which must be used on the four-stroke engine. This makes the two-stroke type simple and virtually trouble-free in this area. Two-stroke engines were once considered less efficient than the four-stroke type because gasoline and oil had to be mixed in right proportions by the user; this inconvenience has now been eliminated by automatic oil-feed systems.

Jawa, Kawasaki, Suzuki, and other manufacturers employ special oil-injection systems which supply gasoline and oil from separate tanks to the carburetor. As the throttle

A six-volt battery, showing leads disconnected and one cell cap removed so that distilled water can be added to the electrolyte. (*Author*)

is opened to increase engine speed, the volume of oil delivered changes proportionately, so that at all times the gasoline and oil mixture, with air, is correct. Nevertheless, some riders still prefer to mix their own.

Inside every engine some parts are constantly rubbing against other parts when the machine is running. Such rubbing is called friction, and friction creates heat which causes metal parts to expand. In order to eliminate as much of the friction heat as possible, all moving parts of an engine are fitted into plain bearings and roller bearings, and all bearings are lubricated with oil. Without internal lubrication, an engine could not operate, since the parts would quickly seize because of the heat.

Lubrication of bearings and other parts in a two-stroke engine is taken care of by oil being injected into the crankcase, but in the four-stroke engine an oil pump feeds oil where it is needed. The oil pump is usually located in the bottom of the crankcase, and as soon as the engine is started, the pump begins to force oil through passages drilled in various parts of the engine.

What makes the four-stroke engine more complex mechanically than the two-stroke is the valve gear. The valves themselves are flat disks with long stems, which are connected to rockers, which in turn are connected to the pushrods, which are moved by cams located on a shaft inside the engine. When the valves are on top of the cylinder, the engine is called an overhead valve type (OHV); when a gear-driven shaft operates the cams, rockers, and the valves at the top of the cylinder, the engine is an overhead cam type (OHC). In special instances an engine is equipped with

The coil connection to the sparkplug is clearly shown on this 90 cc two-stroke engine. Note air-cooling fins on cylinder and engine head.

(*American Jawa*)

double overhead cams (DOHC). All valves are fitted with strong steel valve springs to keep them seated tightly against the cylinder ports during the compression stroke.

The Carburetor

The carburetor mixes gasoline and air in the correct proportion of one part gasoline to fifteen parts air, and delivers this mixture, in the form of a vapor, to the cylinder. When the air portion is greater (as adjusted at the carburetor), the mixture is a lean one; when the gasoline portion is greater, the mixture is rich. On some motorcycles an air-control lever is provided on the handlebar, or on the carburetor itself, and serves as a convenient mixture control.

Many motorcycle engines have one cylinder, and this cylinder will use one carburetor, or carb as they are called by riders. If the machine has a two-cylinder engine, the two cylinders may be fed by a single carb, or each cylinder may have its own carb.

Operation of a carburetor is simple. Gasoline is supplied to a bowl and is fed to the carburetor's mixing chamber through a small passage. This passage is controlled, as is the supply of gasoline to the bowl itself. At the other side of the carb, air is allowed to enter the mixing chamber.

In order to increase the flow of the fuel mixture, the rider twists the throttle on the right handlebar. This action lifts the needle inside the carb, allowing more fuel and air to pass. To keep the engine idling at slow speed, the throttle is closed clockwise; to speed up the engine, the throttle is turned counterclockwise.

On the average motorcycle, the carburetor consists of the following parts:

The main jet, which controls the mixture ratio when the throttle is opened wide.

The throttle needle (or valve), which affects the mixture ratio at mid-settings of the throttle; used to enrich or weaken the mixture.

The idle jet or pilot air screw, which controls the idling speed of the engine and is also used to enrich or weaken the mixture.

The air-control level (if provided), which acts as a choke to cut off air to the carburetor, thus enriching the mixture; used during cold-weather startups. After the engine is started, this control must be opened.

The priming plunger or "tickler," which, when pressed down, floods the carb to provide a temporary rich mixture for starting.

While the average motorcycle carburetor is a simple device with very few moving parts, its adjustments are fairly critical and for this reason the rider should not try any readjustments of the settings unless he is experienced.

Because both the gasoline and the air drawn into the carb are liable to contain dirt, fuel and air filters are fitted to the carburetion system. In order to have an efficient fuel and air feed, these filters must be cleaned at regular intervals.

The Ignition System

The ignition system ignites the fuel mixture inside the

Kick starting a motorcycle engine is a simple procedure: kick lever is positioned at the top of its stroke so that compression resistance can be felt, ignition is switched on, and the lever kicked down through the stroke as the right hand twists the throttle slightly open. (Author)

cylinder. Basically, two systems are used: the pure magneto, and the battery and coil system. Both systems produce a powerful electrical spark at the sparkplug when the piston has compressed the fuel mixture.

The magneto is used mostly on competition-type motorcycles because these models do not require electrical energy for a light and horn since such items on a racing machine serve no purpose and add unnecessary weight. The magneto is located at one side end of the crankshaft (in the case of the BMW, it operates off the camshaft) and consists of a permanent magnet rotor which revolves, as the engine is running, inside a fixed stator, coil, and breaker points. The moment the engine is kicked over, the magneto is capable of producing a powerful spark.

Magneto systems are employed also on regular street and touring machines; in such cases the magneto serves for the ignition system and the battery and generator supply energy for the lights and horn.

When the battery and coil are used, the generator or the alternator become vital parts of the ignition system. The generator and the alternator produce current when the engine is running and thus charge the battery, replacing energy drained off by the lights and horn.

Electrical energy in the form of a direct current (dc) is stored in the battery. As this current is used, the battery is drained. To replenish the battery, the generator or alternator produce an alternating current (ac) as soon as the engine is started, and a rectifier changes this current into dc in order to charge the battery. A voltage regulator, which essentially consists of a set of breaker points, acts to regulate the current to the battery so that there will be no under- or overcharging. The advantage of an alternator is that it operates efficiently at high revolutions and is capable of charging the battery even while the engine is idling. Generators are also called dynamos.

When the machine is equipped with an electric starter,

On this MV Agusta the exhaust pipe and muffler system on each side is carried along the bottom of the engine and rear axle. Note left-side kick starter, carb, and tire tread. (*Author*)

as on the Kawasaki F3, Moto-Guzzi, Jawa Tatran, and others, the energy needed for starting is drawn from the battery to a generatorlike unit, which in many instances doubles as a starter and as a generator. But as soon as the engine starts, the generator begins charging the battery, which has been drained quite heavily by the starter operation.

The battery itself is a set of negative (—) and positive (+) plates with separators contained in a hard rubber case. At each side of this rubber case are two terminals marked plus and minus, to which the respective plates are connected. The case is filled with an electrolyte solution of sulfuric acid and distilled water to a level that just covers the top of the plates. One terminal of the battery is grounded (connected) to the frame of the motorcycle, while the other feeds the ignition and electrical system. Depending on the machine, either the plus or the minus side may be grounded, and care is needed therefore not to reverse the connections and the polarity when reconnecting the battery.

The high-tension current needed for the spark to ignite the fuel mixture inside the cylinder is created in the secondary winding of the coil. The flow of current in the primary winding of the coil is interrupted when the breaker points (timed by a cam) open, thus creating the high-tension current used by the sparkplug. The condenser is part of the system and is usually located near the breaker points, and eliminates any electrical arcing. The points open and close for every spark that takes place at the sparkplug.

The entire continuity for ignition depends, of course, on the ignition key being in the on position.

The Starter

The usual starter mechanism on motorcycles is the kick starter. The kick starter level is kicked downward by the rider, and gears inside the engine turn the crankshaft over and thus start the sequence of piston and valve, and carburetion and ignition operation. The actual method of kick starting is to position the lever at the top of its stroke and feel for compression in the cylinder, then switch on the igni-

Upswept exhausts with heat shields are featured on the Benelli 125 Cobra Scrambler. (*Cosmopolitan Motors*)

tion and kick down on the lever sharply. Complete startup procedures are explained in another chapter of this book.

The Cooling System

Even though the oil inside the engine acts to keep the moving parts cool, additional cooling must be provided. Automobile engines are generally cooled by water circulating around the cylinders, but on most motorcycle engines air is used for cooling purposes. Air cooling becomes more efficient when the cylinder and the cylinder head are designed with rows of fins; on some models even the crankcase is finned for maximum cooling of the hot oil. To prevent a buildup of heat, the machine should not stand still too long once the engine is started.

Since the crankcase is the lowest part of the motorcycle, some models used for competition are fitted with a skidplate, made of heavy-gauge steel, which protects the underside of the engine.

Other Units

In order to have a quiet-running motorcycle, mufflers and exhaust pipes are attached to the exhaust ports of the cylinders. These pipes are usually positioned along the bottom of the engine and rear axle on street and touring machines, but on sports and racing models the pipes are swept upward so that they will not scrape the ground when the machine is leaned over in a sharp curve or when it is riding over rough ground and through mud and water. On these sports models special metal shields are fitted over the pipes to protect the rider's legs from burns.

Motorcycles used for woods or trail riding are equipped with spark arrestors in the exhaust system to prevent possible sparks from igniting dry grass and underbrush.

3

The Clutch and Gear System

A motorcycle engine supplies the power, or torque, but it would not be practical to attempt to use this power directly at the rear wheel because the crankshaft and the rear wheel could not be made to turn together smoothly from a standing position. In order to accomplish a smooth transition in applying power from the engine, a clutching or coupling device is used together with a set of gears that permit an easy start and a progressive pickup in speed.

Motorcycle engines are designed with the clutch and gearbox as one integral unit that saves weight and space. In simple terms, the clutching device is located between the crankshaft and the set of three, four, five, or six gears of different sizes. The rider starts up the engine with the gears in the neutral position, meaning that all gears are free and not engaged to any other gear, and he then selects a gear that will start the machine rolling from a standstill position. But before selecting the gear, the rider uses the clutch so that the rotating crankshaft of the engine is turning freely—and so are the gears. Now, with the first gear selected and the engine running, the rider merely engages the selected gear and the motorcycle begins to move forward at a slow pace.

All other gears are similarly selected and engaged by the clutch, until finally the motorcycle is moving at cruising speed.

The Clutch

Motorcycle clutches are usually of the friction type, com-

The parts and operation of a clutch are shown in this view of a Suzuki T500 multiplate wet-type: (1) clutch spring, (2) pressure plate, (3) cork plates, (4) steel plates, (5) primary gear, (6) clutch housing, (7) clutch lever on handlebar, (8) clutch cable, (9) release screw, (10) screw guide, (11) pushrod, (12) release rod, and (13) adjusting screw. (*U.S. Suzuki*)

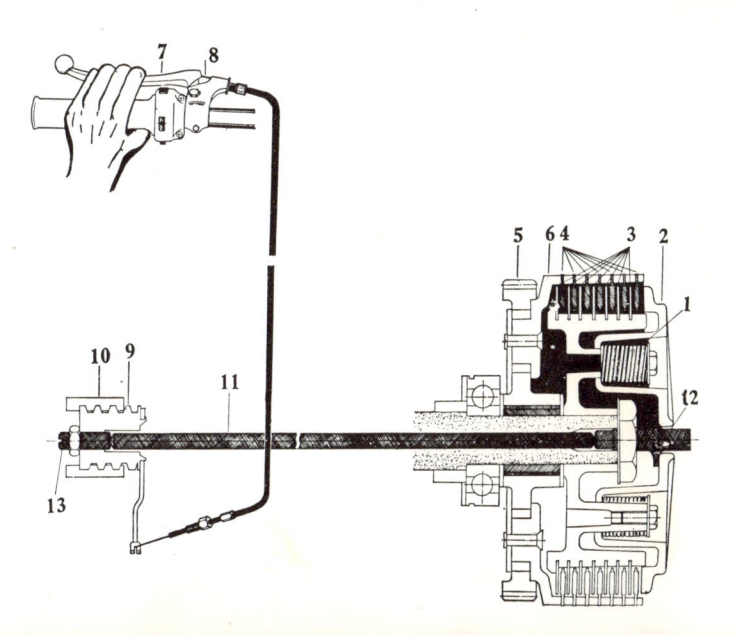

posed of flat circular plates or a set of plates. The entire assembly may be enclosed in an oil bath, in which case the clutch is called a wet type, or the plates may be operating without the oil bath, in which case it is a dry-type clutch.

The clutch operates to join two plates. By forcing the plates together slowly, friction finally causes the two plates to turn as one. Thus, in the engaged position the clutch plates are held against each other by expanded springs. When the rider wants to disengage the clutch in order to select another gear, the clutch plates are pulled apart (as the rider squeezes the clutch lever on the left handlebar), so that the driven plate is separated from the drive plate inside the clutch mechanism. Once the gear is selected, the

In this exploded view of a Benelli four-speed gearbox, the neutral and progressive gear positions are indicated diagrammatically.

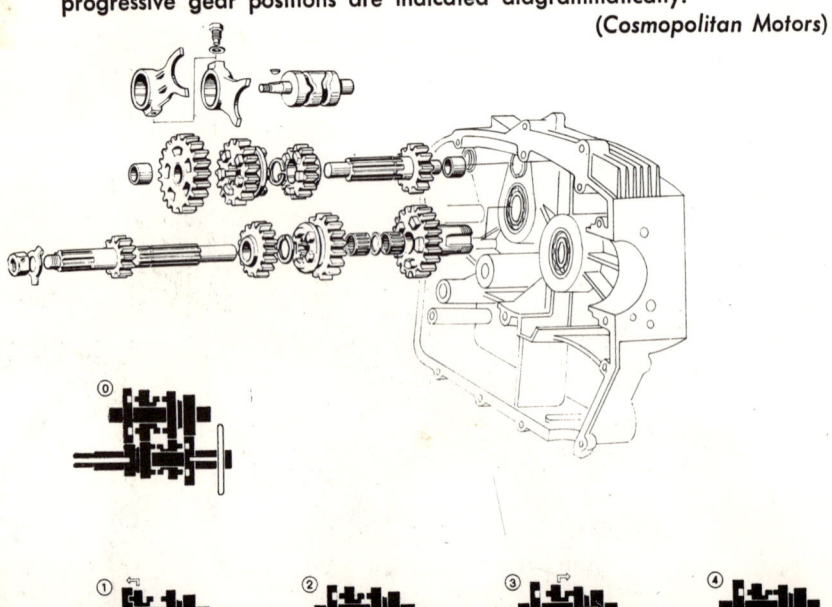

(Cosmopolitan Motors)

rider slowly releases the clutch lever, the springs force the clutch plates smoothly together, and engine torque is applied efficiently to the selected gear.

The clutch actually acts to interrupt engine power to the gears, so that any one gear can be positioned for driving purposes.

The Gears

The purpose of the gearbox or transmission is to provide the necessary gears for the forward speeds—from three to as many as six gears. In principle, the rider disengages the clutch and then selects or lines up two gears by moving the gear shift lever with his foot, and then engages the clutch to cause the selected gears to drive the machine.

The idea is to transmit the power of the rotating crank-

The main chain on this high-performance CZ 250/360 Motocross model is fitted over a robust drive sprocket on the rear wheel and adjusted for correct tension. (American Jawa)

shaft of the engine to a set of gears, and then pass this power on to the rear wheel. A primary chain (on some models a set of small gears are used instead of a chain) turns the input shaft inside the gearbox: crankshaft torque is passed through the clutch to the input shaft. The input shaft drives another shaft which is fitted with the forward speed gears (first, second, third, fourth) which match another set of gears fitted to the second shaft; thus any set of gears can be meshed, and when the clutch is engaged the rotation will be transmitted to the output shaft.

In this way, then, a drive gear is used to transmit its turning force to another gear called the driven gear. Depending on the design of the clutch and gearbox, usually a small

Located on the rear fork, adjusters provide for correctly tensioning the chain. On this MV Agusta, the adjuster is located just behind the rear axle bolt. (*Author*)

sprocket is fitted to the end of the output shaft, and the main chain (sometimes called the secondary chain) drives the large sprocket on the rear wheel.

The performance capabilities of a motorcycle depend largely on the size of gears and sprockets used. For example, for greater pulling power the driven gear must be larger so that the smaller drive gear can turn the large gear slowly but with full power. As speed is gained, less engine power will be needed to continue the rotation, and finally the drive gear and the driven gear may be of the same size, which is said to be a 1 to 1 (1:1) ratio.

By inverting the arrangement—when the driven gear is

Top view cutaway shows famed BMW opposed cylinder engine and shaft drive. The shaft drive system is also employed on such motorcycles as the MV Agusta and Moto-Guzzi. (BMW—Butler & Smith)

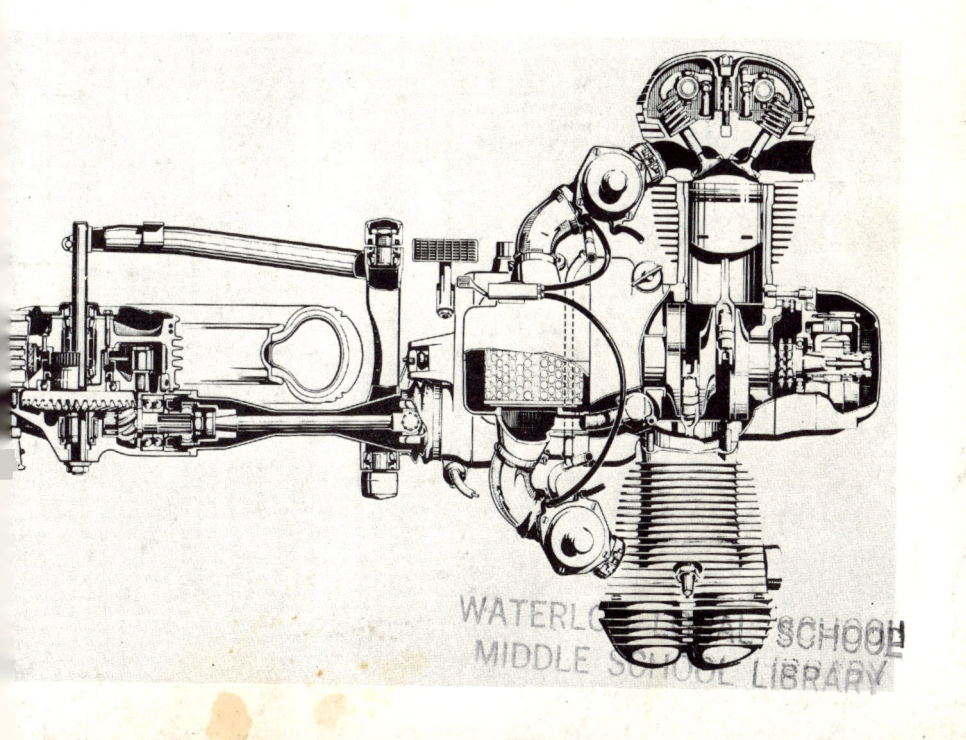

smaller than the drive gear—the opposite result is achieved: weaker pulling power but very high speed.

The term "gear ratio" is often used in connection with the gearbox of a motorcycle. It simply means that the manufacturer has equipped the machine with a set of gears designed to fit the power output of the engine for special purposes. Basically, a close ratio is a set of gears where the number of teeth between one gear and the next are closely related, used on street and touring motorcycles; a wide ratio is the opposite setup found usually on sports machines, where pulling power at slow speeds is assured through widely spaced gear combinations.

Engine power and gearing thus contribute to overall performance of the motorcycle. Add to this a variety of rear wheel sprocket sizes, and performance is further affected.

Because stresses are imposed on the main chain when the motorcycle is running, an adjustment for the chain tension is provided at the rear of the rear wheel fork or swing arm. The usual slack required is about one inch at midpoint of the chain, and the reason for the slack is to prevent possible damage to the drive components. A chain guard is fitted over the chain to prevent dirt from splashing the rider's leg.

On some motorcycles the rear wheel is driven by a shaft, as in the case of the BMW, Moto-Guzzi, and MV Agusta. On the BMW, for example, the operation is as follows: From the driving flange of the transmission the drive shaft transmits power to the meshed coupler gear, which is keyed to the rear axle drive pinion. Splining on the crown gear shaft transmits the power, terminating in driving the rear wheel axle.

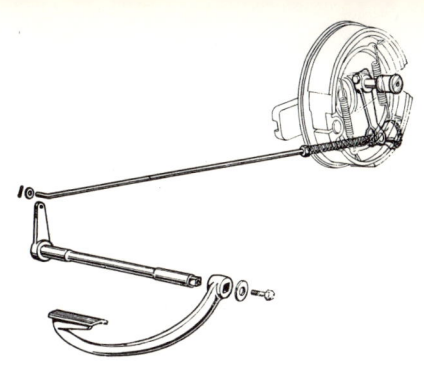

The interior of the rear brake assembly on a Benelli. Pressure on the foot pedal pulls the rod and expands the brake shoes against the drum contained in the hub (not shown). (*Cosmopolitan Motors*)

All gearboxes have a neutral position in which no gear is positioned for driving; this is the only position in which the clutch can be released by the rider while the engine is running and not have the machine move forward. Many gears are arranged with another neutral position, either between the second and third gears, or between the third and fourth. Also, if the machine is specifically designed for use with a sidecar, the gearbox may be fitted with a reverse gear, which can be used for backing up purposes, as in an automobile.

Since the rider needs two feet to balance the motorcycle when moving slowly through heavy traffic, the value of a foot-operated gear changer and hand-operated clutch becomes obvious. Early American motorcycles employed the reverse setup—hand shift and foot clutch—which was not too practical and was the cause of many accidents.

A unique automatic declutching device is used on the Jawa models. After the machine starts up in first gear, the rider merely shifts gears without bothering to use the clutch lever.

Most low-powered minibikes and scooters utilize the very

simple and practical centrifugal-type clutch which also operates automatically. The speed of the engine regulates the coupling and uncoupling of the clutch; thus, merely by closing the throttle momentarily the clutch is disengaged, and, after the next gear is selected and engine power is applied, the clutch automatically engages to drive the machine.

Motorcycle manufacturers have not standardized the location of the gearshift lever and the rear wheel brake pedal. On some machines the gear lever is on the left side of the engine, while on others it is on the right. Generally the first gear is one position up on the front part of the lever, then down for neutral and all other gears, and this holds true usually whether the lever is on the left or right side. The brake pedal is located on the opposite side from the gear lever. The clutch lever, however, is always on the left handlebar, and the throttle is always on the right side.

Note ball bearings in this Benelli front hub and brake shoe assembly. (Cosmopolitan Motors)

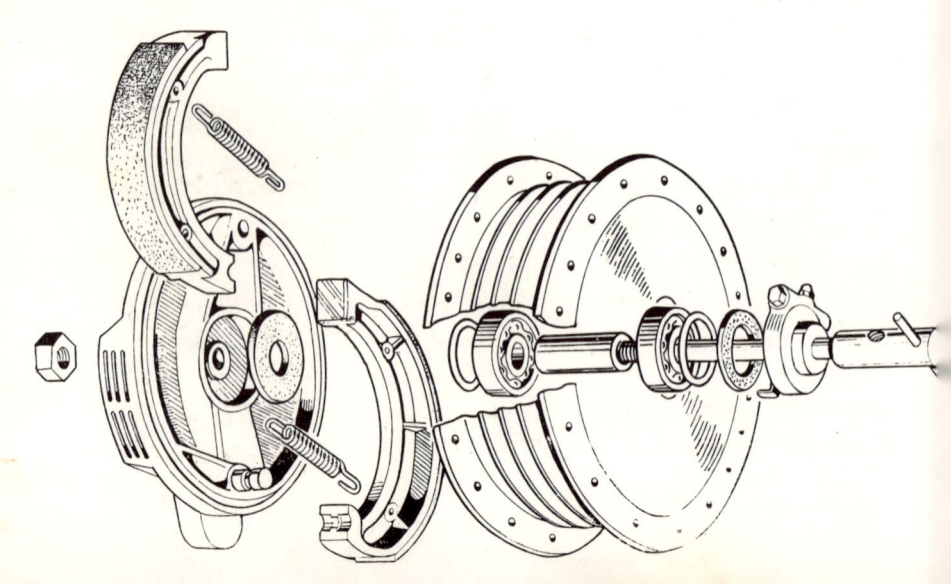

Switch located at front brake shoe lever activates rear stoplight. (*Author*)

Braking System

Because of its light weight, more than adequate engine power, and gearing, the average motorcycle is capable of sudden bursts of speed. This means that the brakes must be excellent.

The usual arrangement is for a hand-operated front wheel brake, and a foot-operated rear wheel brake. The front wheel brake lever is located on the right handlebar, so that the rider need merely release the throttle and squeeze the brake lever. If the gearshift lever is on the left side of the engine, the rear wheel brake pedal will be on the right side; if the gear lever is on the right, as on many British and Italian models, the brake pedal is on the left.

The brakes themselves are operated either independently or together, and the stopping ability of the machine depends on such factors as types of tires, tire pressure, road surface, and type and size of brake area.

Most machines are equipped with internal expanding brake shoes which are forced against the inside of a drum. The hand lever is connected to the front brake arm by a cable, while the rear brake pedal may be connected either by a cable or a rod. Some manufacturers are providing hydraulic brake systems like those used on automobiles; others are experimenting with the highly efficient disk-type brakes, as on the four-cylinder MV Agusta.

The usual method of brake operation is for the rider to apply the rear brake first, then the front. Many skillful riders use both brakes at the same time for quick stops; in either case, riders are cautious in braking while the machine is in a turn since any overuse of brakes may cause a spill.

Sales brochures provide the motorcycling enthusiast with technical data about primary and secondary drive, gear ratios, and also with information about the stopping ability of the particular model. On the average, a bike weighing around 300 to 400 pounds will be able to stop in from 30 to 39 feet from a speed of 30 miles per hour, depending on the road surface conditions.

Whenever the rear brake pedal is used, the rear stoplight is activated by a special brake switch. Some models are fitted with a stoplight switch on the front wheel brake as well.

4

The Frame and the Suspension

The frame of a motorcycle, like the chassis of an automobile, supports the engine, clutch, gearbox, fuel tank, seat, and all the other parts that make up the machine. The suspension, on the other hand, supports the entire machine on the two wheels and also provides comfort for the rider by absorbing as much of the road roughness as possible.

Frame

Prior to the improvement of metal alloys, motorcycle frames were bulky, heavy tubes welded together so that the rest of the machinery could be fitted in. The results were always the same: a big and heavy motorcycle with power that was not suited to its weight.

Modern technology is producing seamless steel tubing of finest quality which, as used on motorcycles, produces a

53

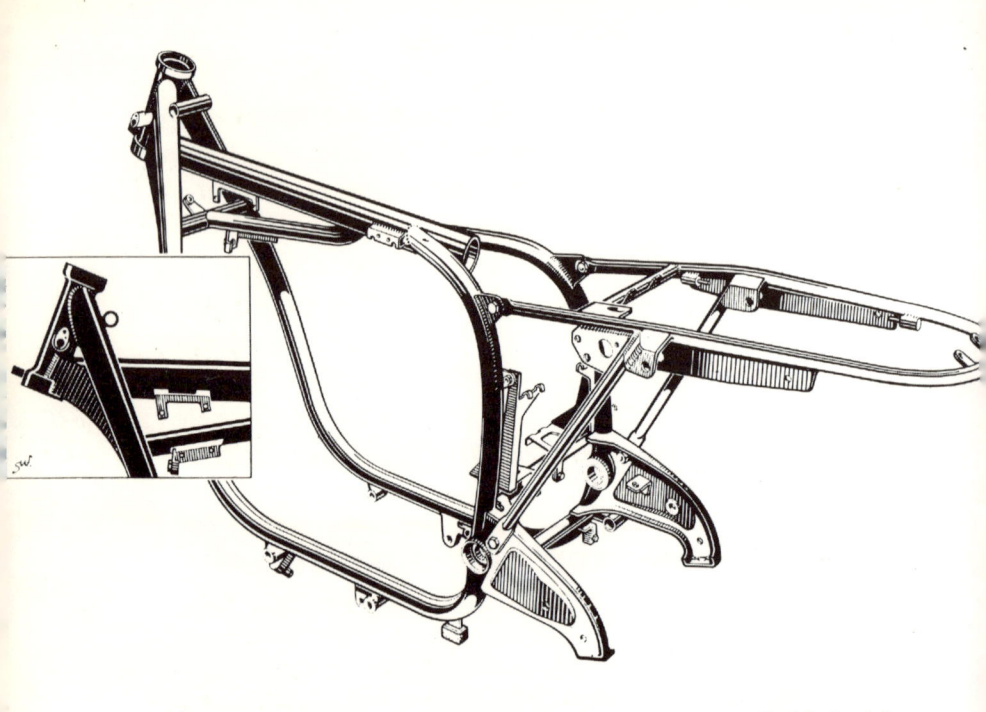

The advanced BMW cradle-type tubular frame is composed of bolted front and rear sections. Insert shows steering head which supports front fork and handlebars. (BMW—*Butler & Smith*)

torsionally rigid yet light frame capable of withstanding the imposed loads and stresses.

Most recent developments in frame structures are the square or rectangular section type, although the tube type still continues, and the spine-type in which two steel pressings are welded together. To isolate vibrations, some manufacturers use rubber bushes to mount the engine into the frame.

Front Fork

Like a bicycle, the motorcycle uses a front fork into

which the front wheel is mounted along with the front brake mechanism contained within the hub. On some models the hub will contain the speedometer drive gear (some speedometers are driven by the gearbox shaft).

A combination of hydraulic and coil spring shock absorbers is fitted on the front fork telescoping tubes; these are enclosed to protect the mechanism from dirt and dust.

The steering head of the frame supports the front fork and the handlebar assembly, which may be further provided with a steering damper which the rider may loosen or tighten to suit riding conditions.

Rear Fork

The rear wheel, with the hub containing the rear brake

Lightweight pressed steel frame of a Benelli (engine removed) with enclosed telescopic front fork and rear swing-arm fork.

(*Cosmopolitan Motors*)

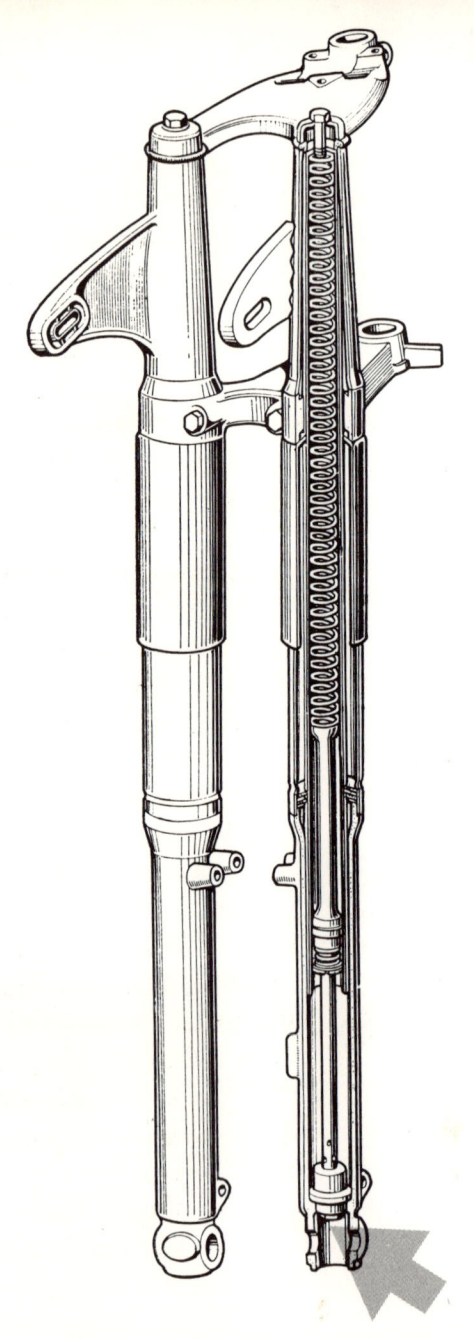

Cutaway view of the Benelli front fork. Arrow indicates oil drain hole used when servicing the hydraulic shock absorber system.
(Cosmopolitan Motors)

mechanism, and the sprocket, are mounted in the rear fork or swing arm, which is designed on the pivoting principle—the fork is fitted to the frame just behind the engine, and the hydraulic and coil spring shock absorbers connect it to the upper portion of the frame extension. The rear wheel is thus permitted to lift and drop when riding over rough road surfaces while the shock absorber system smoothens the oscillations. Some rear suspension systems are provided with adjusters for stiffening or softening the ride for the passenger.

The modern motorcycle literally floats over the roads, while its old counterpart was known to produce severe cases of weakened kidneys. Old-time riders actually wore "kidney belts" to ease the continuous shocks to the body produced by the very rigid suspensions. About the only shock absorbers on early motorcycles were the seat springs and a leaf spring fitted to the front fork—the rest being taken up by the cushioning effect supplied by the tires.

Wheels and Tires

Motorcycle wheels are of the spoked type, like bicycle wheels, and rim size is usually 18 inches except on special machines. The wheel hubs are fitted with ball bearings, and these must be repacked with grease at specified intervals, usually every 10,000 to 15,000 miles of riding.

To ensure road-holding stability, the wheels are carefully aligned and balanced, and the spokes are correctly tensioned to eliminate twisting of the rim.

Tires are designed for specific kinds of riding. For average city and road riding, a fairly fine-tread design is preferred; for competition riding, a variety of heavy, cleated tires are used.

According to tire type, purpose, and machine weight, tire pressures range from 18 pounds per square inch (psi) to as high as 33 psi.

Fenders

The purpose of fenders is simply to keep the road dirt from splashing against the machine and the rider, but the width and style of fenders depends on how the motorcycle will be used. For riding in the woods and on trails, fenders are usually fitted high off the wheels to prevent mud and twigs from jamming the wheels and causing loss of control. Street machines use fenders that are sleek in design and fairly close to the wheels. For certain types of racing, the fenders are removed completely from the bike.

Fuel Tank

The steel tank, carrying fuel for the engine, is mounted topside on the frame and, depending on the model and purpose, may hold from 1.5 to 4 gallons of gasoline. Tank sizes and shapes vary with different motorcycles. Plastic or metal tubes carry fuel by gravity feed from the tank to the carburetors, which are positioned below the tank.

On two-stroke engines using the automatic oil-feed system, the oil tank is usually located separately under the tank and at one side of the frame.

Saddle and Toolbox

The modern long saddle or seat, utilizing leather or vinyl covering over foam rubber, is designed for maximum com-

Close-up of a BSA fuel tank, streamlined for speed and appearance, with chromed filler cap and rubber kneepads adding to the dress-up.

(BSA—East)

fort and generally provides room for the rider and one passenger.

The toolbox and tools are usually located under the hinged seat, but on some models the toolbox is mounted at the side of the frame under the saddle.

Footrests and Stands

Foot supports for the rider and passenger are provided in the form of footpegs or, on some heavy machines, with actual footboards.

When the motorcycle is not being used, it must be set up on a stand, and for this a rugged center stand (fitted to the frame) is provided onto which the machine is lifted easily. For temporary standing, a sidestand or "jiffy stand" may

59

A Benelli on its well-positioned center stand. Note the leg guards fitted over the exhaust pipe, and the sturdy footpegs. (*Cosmopolitan Motors*)

also be fitted to the bottom of the frame; the rider simply kicks the stand outward, then leans the bike on it.

When the machine is on its center stand, either the front or the rear wheel can be lifted an inch or two off the ground, and this provides a convenience to the rider when working on some part of the machine.

Crashbars and Exhaust Leg Guards

Some riders fit chrome-plated tubular bars at right angles to the frame and just ahead of the engine to serve as leg protection in the event of a spill.

On motorcycles where the exhaust pipes are carried very high, special metal guards fitted over the pipes protect the rider's thighs from heat and possible burns.

On trail and woods machines, spark arrestors within the exhaust pipes prevent the possibility of starting a dry grass or brush fire as the bike is traveling over such terrain.

Windshields, Racks, Saddlebags

Heavy plastic transparent shields may be fitted to the front fork and handlebars to act as a wind, rain, and dirt deflector.

A luggage rack fitted over the rear wheel fender is used for carrying small objects, while small or large saddlebags, usually attached to the rear upper frame and wheel braces, serve for carrying equipment on long trips.

Rearview mirrors may be fitted either to the windshield or to the handlebars for safety purposes.

5

Switches, Controls, and Indicators

To operate a motorcycle safely and with some degree of skill, the rider must know the location of every control level, pedal, switch, light, and indicator. The fumbling rider, the one who must look down to see whether his foot is on the peg or on the brake pedal, is a menace to himself and to others. In other words, the rider must handle the machine as naturally as if he had been doing it all his life, and the only way this familiarity can be achieved is by practice in using the controls and switches.

There are three areas for the rider to understand:
1. The switches for ignition, lights, and signaling systems.
2. The major controls for operating the motorcycle, consisting of the throttle, the clutch, the gearshift, and the brake levers.
3. The indicators which inform him how the engine

A Jawa 350 cc general-purpose motorcycle as seen from the rider's position in the saddle. Note ignition switch in headlight above speedometer, and the throttle setscrew in right handlebar with its reinforced cross member. (*Author*)

is operating, road speed, electrical system, and other conditions, all in the form of lights or clock-like dials.

Switches and Indicators

These are grouped together here because they are usually interconnected. In order to close the ignition circuit and make it possible to start the engine, the ignition key is

63

inserted into the ignition switch and set at the *on* position; at this time the ignition light will light up to indicate that the battery is draining. On certain model machines the oil pressure light and the gear position light (neutral) will also light up. As soon as the engine is started, these lights turn off. On some models the indicating lights are placed on top of the headlight, where the rider can see them readily, or they may be arranged within the speedometer housing.

The horn button is usually on the left handlebar near the grip, and immediately next to it is the switch for the low/high headlight beam, which can be operated after the ignition switch is turned to one side; if the key is turned to the other side, only the parking light in the headlight and the taillight will switch on.

A switch is fitted at the foot-operated rear brake pedal so that when the pedal is used the rear stoplight flashes in warning.

Not to be outdone by automobiles, many motorcycles are equipped with directional signal lights, which are operated by a switch located on the handlebar, to indicate that the rider intends to turn, and which direction.

On some model motorcycles an ammeter is provided to indicate the rate of charge or discharge of the battery.

Aside from these indicators, motorcycles are also equipped with a speedometer which is usually fitted in the top of the headlight and divided into 10 or 20 mile-per-hour segments, indicating the machine's road speed. An odometer, or mileage counter, is contained within the speedometer to indicate distance covered.

Like some sports cars, a motorcycle may be equipped

with a tachometer, which indicates the speed at which the engine crankshaft is turning, in revolutions per minute (rpm). A red-marked segment on the face of the tachometer warns the rider that the engine rpms are in the dangerous area, where they should not be held for more than a few seconds.

Major Controls

As a steering control, the handlebar is taken for granted,

Grouped instrumentation on a BSA, with speedometer and tachometer mounted side by side, and with oil, ignition, and main beam warning lights. (BSA—East)

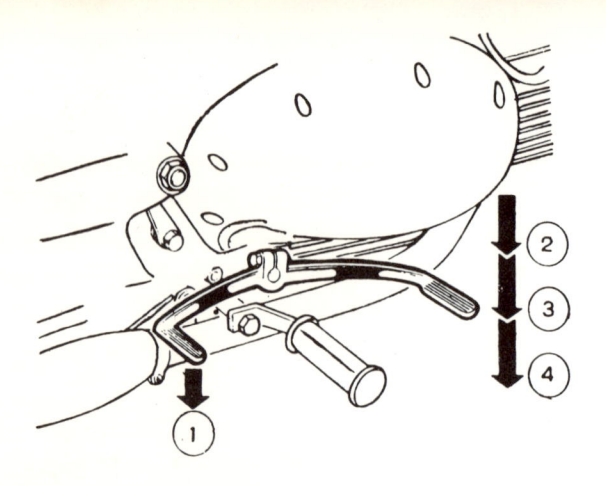

The four-speed Benelli gearshifting sequence is: heel presses down for first gear, then toe presses down for second, third, and fourth gear.
(*Cosmopolitan Motors*)

yet designs of handlebars vary considerably—wide, narrow, straight, curved, and cross-barred. The very high "ape hangers" have been legally ruled as unsafe, and no handlebar may be higher than fifteen inches from the saddle top. The point, however, is that the best handlebar for the particular motorcycle is the one which was designed by the manufacturer's engineers and not the homemade grotesque styles which endanger the rider's safety.

The throttle twist-grip, which controls the speed of the engine, is always located in the right handlebar and is usually spring-loaded to return to the closed position if the rider releases his hold on the grip. On some throttles a small setscrew can be used to stiffen the throttle action or even lock it in any position. This is generally used only when tuning the engine or on long steady speed runs.

The clutch lever, which is used to couple or uncouple the engine from the gears, is located on the left handlebar. When the motorcycle is started from standstill, the clutch lever is squeezed to disengage the clutch plates and permit selection of a gear. After the gear is selected, the clutch is released slowly, and then engaged to start the machine rolling. The clutch must be disengaged every time a gearshift is required. An automatic clutching action is provided on some Jawa models, so that the lever may be ignored after the first gear clutching is completed.

The gearshift lever, which selects the required gear, is foot-operated and may be located on either the left or right side of the engine. On the Jawa and BMW machines, the shift is located on the left side, while on such machines as BSA, MV Agusta, Benelli, and others, the shift is on the right side. The movement of the lever is up and down, either by toe or heel action; neutral gear position may be reached in one movement from first or second gear, but to reach neutral from third, fourth, or fifth gear, the shift lever must be used that many times.

If the gearshift lever is located on the left side, the rear brake pedal is on the right side of the engine, and the brake is on the left side if the shift is on the right.

The front brake lever is hand-operated and is located on the right handlebar.

The two brakes should be employed simultaneously, but the brakes should never be used forcefully when the motorcycle is in a turn.

6

Important Maintenance

Motorcycle riders are often considered fanatical for the way they take care of their machines, which they do probably because they are so intimately related to their bikes that the slightest misadjustment is felt in overall performance.

One thing is certain—without proper maintenance, any machine will eventually deteriorate and its performance will suffer. An engine may be ruined by running it without enough oil to lubricate the internal parts. To prevent such damages, the motorcycle manufacturers provide specific instructions for taking care of the particular machine, and expert riders always observe these instructions.

One of the most important things to check is the oil level in the crankcase; the level must be kept to the mark indicated. A four-stroke engine is usually provided with a dipstick with a low and high level mark, while the two-stroke engine has a removable screw or plug at which point the gearbox oil level can be checked. An engine cannot operate without oil. Lack of oil will cause quick overheating and finally a "freeze up" or seizing of the parts. If a defective gasket at some part of the engine is allowing oil to leak out, the experienced rider will notice this in the form of oil spots on the ground under the engine and will quickly remedy the condition.

The fuel tank should be kept full to eliminate condensation, and if the machine is not in use, the fuel flow valve should be shut to prevent possible fuel leakage. Both the carburetor air filter and the fuel line filter should be checked and cleaned at specified intervals.

To make sure that electrical power will be available, it is important to check the electrolyte level in the battery; without a properly charged battery, the ignition, lighting, and horn will suffer. The plus and minus terminal connections on the battery must also be kept clean and solid.

Every so often the timing of the spark and the condition of the breaker points and condenser must be checked and adjusted to the required clearances.

Tires and tire pressures should not be taken for granted but should be checked regularly. If the treads are badly worn, they will not hold up in sharp curves and may cause a spill. Poor handling of a motorcycle is often due to badly underinflated tires.

Too much slack in the control cables or rods can create dangerous conditions while riding—particularly in connection with brakes, clutch, and carburetors.

The correct adjustment of the headlight is as important as a properly operating rear stoplight, and both should be checked during daylight and not after darkness when a lightless machine becomes a menace in the streets or on the roads.

At specified mileages the condition of the brake shoes and the drive chain must be inspected. If these are worn, they should be replaced, and then adjusted.

After the motorcycle has been operated for approximately 3,000 miles, the valve rocker clearances on a four-stroke engine should be checked and adjusted. Improved performance will be noticed immediately. At this mileage many riders take apart the carburetor, clean all the parts, and then carefully reassemble the unit and adjust it.

After about 10,000 miles of riding, the wheel bearings will need repacking with grease, as specified by the manufacturer, and the engine mountings—the large bolts which hold the engine in the frame—should be checked for tightness.

This kind of periodic checking and adjusting is called preventive maintenance and is intended to reduce the possibility of trouble developing on the road. Yet in spite of the best care, the machine may unexpectedly develop trouble, and to help the rider trace the possible causes, the manufacturer provides a troubleshooting chart in the *Owner's Manual*. This chart lists the problems that can most likely happen, and also outlines the possible causes and gives the remedies. Most problems can be listed in three areas:

1. Electrical. These problems deal with wires and connections, the condition of the battery, the ignition system, and the switches.
2. Fuel. These problems concern the condition of the fuel, the shutoff valves, the filters, and the carb.
3. Mechanical. These problems involve the lubrica-

tion system, the condition of mechanical parts such as valves, gears, shafts, bearings, chains, oil feed, and all related adjustments and clearances.

The ability to recognize the source of trouble is acquired through experience, and the study of a good troubleshooting chart. After solving a few minor problems, the new rider will quickly learn to analyze more involved problems. If the kick starter cannot be moved through its stroke, the indication is that the piston or the bearings have seized because of lack of lubrication, or perhaps that a gear tooth in the starter mechanism is jammed, in which case a push against the gear may free it.

Another telltale sign of trouble in the making is any unusual noise in the engine, gearbox, clutch, hubs, shock absorbers, or in the drive chain or shaft. For example, excessive heat in the hubs or in any part requires an immediate check and adjustment of the brakes.

An erratically swinging speedometer needle indicates that the cable drive needs lubrication.

Poor handling of the motorcycle may be caused by incorrect tire pressure or poor treads, improper alignment of the wheels, lack of fluid in the shock absorbers, extreme tightness or looseness in the steering mechanism; even a loose seat can give the feeling that the machine is out of proper control.

These problems are generally easier to track down than those of carburetion and ignition. For these, the *Owner's Manual* should be consulted, and if the manual states that the machine should be taken to an authorized service representative this is the wise course to follow, since carb and ignition problems may be too complex for the new rider.

7

How to Ride a Motorcycle

While many new riders have a natural urge to speed off on a powerful sleek motorcycle, this can be dangerous. Too many beginners attempt motorcycling without basic preparation, and because of this a good number of them meet with disappointments.

It is a proven fact that the first hour of proper instruction in handling a motorcycle is worth more than the first ten hours of guesswork and experimentation.

Anyone able to ride a bicycle will be able to ride a motorcycle. The skill needed to balance a bicycle is the same skill needed to balance a light or heavy machine, but because of the difference in weight and speeds attained on motorcycles, much more care must be exercised.

The experienced motorcycle rider finds that handling a heavy machine in city traffic or on a country road is in many ways easier than pedaling a bicycle at its much slower speed. The general reasons for this are that the motorcycle is capable of quick bursts of speed and can be brought to a quick stop by its excellent braking system.

The best approach to motorcycling, according to the advice of experts, is to consider right at the start what is dangerous. When the dangers are understood and accepted, the step-by-step techniques of riding a motorcycle are easy to learn and the end result is a good rider enjoying motorcycling.

The following areas, then, are the dangerous ones for the rider:

1. Technical knowledge. Lack of knowledge about the particular machine, its handling characteristics and limitations, and unfamiliarity with its controls.
2. Mechanical faults. If any part of the machine is faulty or out of adjustment, it may cause sudden troubles that can result in a serious accident.
3. Rider's attitude. Being arrogant and inconsiderate, and adding to this attitude high-speed riding with a disregard of the bike's limitations, can create dangerous situations.

These three areas should be of prime importance both to the expert and the beginner. Another dangerous area involves the simple matter of dressing properly for motorcycling: wearing an approved helmet (preferably white) and shatterproof eyeglasses, light-colored jacket, suitable gloves and footwear (open-toed sandals should never be worn). The passenger should also be properly dressed for riding.

One expert also lists "queer" illegal equipment as a general hazard: high handlebars called ape-hangers, and the very narrow ones are both illegal and do not afford good control in an emergency. Open mufflers, with their ear-splitting noise, which frightens pedestrians and car drivers, should likewise be avoided.

According to a famous racer who also uses a motorcycle to ride in town, "It's one thing to be on a dirt race track, where the mad noise is an accepted part of the scene; but to run a bike through traffic down a street with the same bang is stupid. The police *should* give such riders tickets—they deserve it. They *are* a nuisance, and they *are* endangering others."

Since the major problem in motorcycling has to do with speed, the beginner should be introduced to motorcycling first as a passenger. A half hour spent on the back seat of a bike at 30 miles per hour in traffic or on the open road guarantees the sensation of having traveled at 60 miles per hour! Thus the beginner, as a passenger, becomes familiar with the feeling of power and, with a respect for that power, looks forward to handling the machine sensibly himself.

The second major problem in motorcycling is the new rider himself—how to place him in control of the machine? The following simple and proven method is recommended:

Stage 1. Select a fairly steep downhill road at a time when the traffic is very light or preferably nonexistent. Without starting the engine, the beginner should mount the bike and coast downhill, steering and using the brakes as necessary. This practice should be performed first at slow speeds, using the brakes for control of speed, then faster, until the beginning rider feels he is able to handle the machine with perfect control. When the rider applies the brakes, the rear brake is used first, then the front brake is applied for increased braking power. It is dangerous to use the front brake only.

Stage 2. Start the engine, and repeat the entire practice of Stage 1. Now the new rider will become accustomed to the sound and feel of the engine. After rolling downhill several times, he should play the throttle, speeding up the engine as if under actual riding conditions.

Stage 3. Now select an empty parking lot, where the beginner may practice engine startups. Place the bike on its center stand and start the engine several times.

Stage 4. The new rider should now be ready for his first solo ride, and this should be conducted in a large open area, not in a busy traffic street. By this time he will know how to start up the engine, how to use the clutch and the gears, and how to steer and bring the machine to a stop.

NOTE

Neither a minibike nor a regular motorcycle may be operated in city streets without registration, and the rider must also possess a permit or license, depending on state regulations.

During engine startup practice, the new rider must learn about the conditions under which the engine will not start; basically, assuming there is no mechanical breakage in the engine, there are two conditions:

1. No fuel in the tank, or a closed fuel flow valve, and
2. No spark at the sparkplug, because the ignition key was not inserted and the system not activated.

Many riders who forgot these two simple conditions have spent time energetically kicking over the engine in vain. Starting up the engine should be a routine, and seldom should the rider deviate from it. The following is a standard procedure for most motorcycles but may have to be altered slightly to suit special cases:
1. Check fuel tank level and oil level, then open fuel flow valve.
2. Using the tickler, prime the carburetor; follow the manufacturer's instructions for setting the air lever or choke (if provided).
3. Open the throttle partially and kick the engine over two or three times.
4. Insert the ignition key and set the ignition *on* (ignition light glows); the neutral gear position light should also be lit (some models do not have this light). Kick the starter lever sharply.
5. After the engine starts, the choke can be returned to normal (open). The engine should be allowed to warm up for several minutes, ensuring that all internal engine parts are fully lubricated.

And now the new rider faces the most important stage—how to get under way from a standstill, and how to keep going on up to cruising speed, but performing this smoothly, under perfect control, and all the while observing the following four basic rules:

Rule 1—Do not race (rev up) the engine needlessly.

Rule 2—Disengage the clutch before trying to shift gears.

Rule 3—Do not engage clutch abruptly for first gear.

Rule 4—If control is lost for any reason, use the brakes.

With these rules in mind and having practiced the preliminary steps given earlier, the rider should have no problem in the actual start from a standstill.

Step 1. With both feet on the ground, lean the machine slightly away from the side on which the gearshift lever is located and with left hand squeeze the clutch lever. The clutch is now disengaged. During this action be sure to hold the bike still with the front brake lever on the right handlebar. Using the foot, shift into first gear by lifting the gear lever or pressing it down (depending on the model) once.

Step 2. Keeping both feet on the ground, steady the machine. Release right hand holding front brake lever. Open the throttle slightly, and, as engine revolutions increase, begin releasing the clutch lever with left hand. As the machine starts to roll, release the clutch more and open the throttle slightly more. Place both feet on the pegs and start steering the bike straight ahead.

Step 3. As speed increases in first gear, simultaneously close the throttle with the right hand and squeeze the clutch lever with left hand, and then immediately with foot, tap (or lift) the gearshift lever into neutral position. Bike is now rolling free, and the clutch lever can be released.

Step 4. Depending on which side the rear brake pedal is located, the foot presses the brake pedal lightly to bring the machine to a smooth stop. The front brake may also be applied, but not before the rear brake. Just as the motorcycle comes to a stop both feet are placed on the ground, but kept far enough apart so they will not be caught by the footpegs.

In this practice the motorcycle was run in a straight line for a short distance in first gear. This should be repeated, and after this control sequencing is mastered, the new rider should run the bike in large circles, and then in smaller, tighter circles, both to the left and to the right.

WARNING

A motorcycle rider must never, never make a turn unless he first signals and also turns his head to check the traffic for safety.

After this fundamental practice, the now not-so-new rider will feel confident enough to continue shifting through the gears until top gear is reached for cruising, and he will use all controls efficiently so as not to lose control of his machine.

To increase speed, the rider shifts up through the gears; to decrease speed, he shifts down—meaning, from the top gear the lever must be lifted with the foot the required number of times for each gear, each time shifting one gear lower until the neutral position is reached. The clutch must be used, of course, in downshifting as it was used in the upshifting procedure.

The motorcycle is not capable of thinking for the rider; the rider must control the motorcycle. In order to control the machine properly, the rider must use caution and intelligence. For example:

1. The rider must constantly be aware of what surrounds him in traffic, must be aware of the conditions of that traffic, and must train himself to ride far ahead of his machine (as pilots fly "ahead" of their fast-moving airplanes).

2. Remember that speed, coupled with overconfidence, may easily lead to disaster.
3. Driving defensively may not boost the ego, but it certainly eliminates a lot of problems.
4. Remember that the expert riders are the good, safe riders.

8

Selecting the Motorcycle

Motorcycling enthusiasts base their selection of a machine on a variety of factors, yet all the factors revolve around the basic question, "Will this particular motorcycle suit the requirements?"

The requirements begin with the simple consideration whether the machine will be used for general riding or for specialized competition.

If the general riding category is the answer, then the choice must be made from the large number of models called street motorcycles. In this category the machines can be divided into the various weight classifications:

Lightweight machines from the very light models up to about 250 pounds.

Middleweight models between 250 and 400 pounds.

Heavyweight machines which may reach as high as 700 pounds or more.

In connection with weight, it is worth considering the

insurance rates for the motorcycle selected. In New York City, for example, a nominal insurance rate is charged on motorcycles under 300 pounds, but the rates nearly triple when the machine weighs more than 300 pounds.

Engine displacement of street motorcycles varies from 50 cc to 1,200 cc, a factor which affects performance and price. Motorcycles used for competition are considered not only on the basis of engine displacement but also gear

The rugged 95-pound Benelli Dynamo with its single-cylinder two-stroke engine, lights, and horn, is ideal for street, trail, and woods riding at speeds up to 50 mph. Folding handlebars permit bike to be stowed in car trunk or into boat and taken to camping sites. (*Cosmopolitan Motors*)

ratios, wheelbase, and other features which contribute to performance under specialized conditions.

For competition, the choice of models ranges from road racers with very powerful engines to the less powerful but high-performance scramblers, and, in a very special class, the enduro and the woods or trail bikes, some of which may be of the minicycle type.

The selection of a motorcycle may be a simple matter for the enthusiast who has owned several different types of machines and knows exactly what he wants for the kind of riding to be done; the new rider, on the other hand, must

This little Honda features a four-stroke engine which is started by pedaling, after which the automatic clutch simplifies riding. The 106-pound machine travels about 200 miles on one gallon of gasoline.
(American Honda Motor Company)

The Jawa Tatran is a deluxe scooter type with a 125 cc 7-hp engine with engine, lights, and horn, is ideal for street, trail. and woods riding at peformance in full comfort. (*American Jawa*)

proceed carefully and systematically in order not to be disappointed with the eventual choice.

One approach, suggested by experts, is to collect as many sales brochures as possible, study them all very closely, and talk to as many riders as possible who use this type of motorcycle. Then let the whole matter rest for a few weeks, during which time the many features can be evaluated—and only then visit a dealer to buy.

The following is a general classification of motorcycle types:

1. *The Street Motorcycle*

This group covers the majority of machines on the roads and in the streets, and the basic characteristic is that all of these, regardless of engine displacement and weight, are dependable and without quirks. Street bikes are designed for smooth, trouble-free riding at all normal speeds; they are not designed for racing at high speed or for hill climbing or for running over rough terrain.

Street motorcycles are easy to handle and are comfort-

The Jawa 90 cc, single-cylinder two-stroker is an ideal lightweight roadster suitable for street and highway use. Note excellent suspension system. *(American Jawa)*

able. Their gearing is selected for general conditions, fuel consumption is excellent, they are quiet-running, and their appearance is pleasing. The wheelbase is long and thus contributes to riding stability, the fenders are generally wide to prevent dirt from being splashed at the rider, and the suspension system is slightly soft. The exhaust pipes are usually placed under the engine and rear axle.

2. The Competition Scrambler

Both the competition scrambler and the woods or trail machines have very sturdy frames (but not overly heavy ones), a suspension capable of absorbing exceptionally hard shocks, and special gearing.

Depending on the kind of event the bike is intended for,

The Ducati 250 cc is equipped with the efficient overhead cam engine. Note right-foot shift lever and Dell'Orto carburetor.

(Berliner Motor Corporation)

the gear ratio will be wide or close (wide if it is intended for arduous work like a motocross or trail race).

A true road racing machine will be provided with low gearing in first but rather high in top. Ignition control may be manual (rider controlling spark advance and retard), narrow front and wide rear tire. Ground clearance, depending on model, may be high.

A true sprint bike will be provided with a powerful engine and with a gear ratio designed expressly for fast getaways. While some of these machines are capable of acceleration from a standstill position to 60 mph in eight,

The 350 cc Jawa two-cylinder two-stroke model provides the convenience of automatic clutching. The left-side shift lever also acts as a kick starter. Note upswept tailpipes, crashbars, and full-width fenders. (*Author*)

seven, and even six seconds, they are hardly suited for street use.

A scrambler will not have a headlight, horn, battery (it will use a magneto), or fenders, and its engine crankcase will be protected by a strong steel plate or framework. Tires will be of the knobby type, of soft rubber, which would not be practical for street use.

3. The Street Scrambler

It is not clear why this category of motorcycles even exists, since the machine is supposedly designed for street use yet is termed a scrambler, which in turn implies that it is also suitable for some kind of competition. These models are usually equipped with high pipes (sometimes noisy)

The 350 cc Kawasaki twin two-stroke features streamlining with an efficient high-performance engine, suitable for street and long-distance touring. (*Eastern Kawasaki Motorcycle Corporation*)

The 441 cc BSA single-cylinder bike in the middleweight class weighs 306 pounds. Note high ground clearance for sport or touring. (BSA—East)

and high fenders, with a headlight and horn, and knobby rear tires.

The verdict of expert motorcycling enthusiasts is that the street scrambler is misnamed and is aimed at buyers who want a street bike which resembles a scrambler—in short, an ego-booster.

4. The Trail Bike

These are rugged motorcycles, including the minibike and minicycle counterparts, designed for off-the-road riding, and the engine therefore is a low-revving type, usually a single cylinder, for good power at low revolutions for top pulling ability. The gears are widely spaced, which, coupled with the low revving engine, provides best performance for the job at hand.

The steering setup on trail machines is quick and easy.

These models carry lights, horn, speedometer—in short, all the equipment required by law. The engine crankcase is protected with a skidplate.

Since these machines are used on rough terrain, the exhaust pipes are placed high and the footpegs may be spring-loaded so they will snap back to their original positions if displaced by ruts or rocks. Fenders are high to eliminate the possibility of mud or twigs clogging the wheels, and the suspension provides plenty of travel to absorb abnormal

The BMW R75/5 four-stroke opposed twin of 750 cc delivers 57 hp at 6,400 rpm, weighs 421 pounds, and can reach 110 mph. The riding and handling qualities are excellent. Starting is electric, and rear wheel drive is by shaft. (BMW—*Butler & Smith*)

shocks. The most rugged type of clutch is utilized in these machines.

When the rider is actually examining a motorcycle, the following areas should be checked:
1. Is the overall workmanship of the machine, including paint finish and the decorations, excellent, adequate, or poor?
2. Is the engine easy to start? Note whether the toes or the heel of the foot, on the kick starter, strikes any part of the bike during startup procedure.
3. Are the mufflers too noisy?
4. Did any levers bind during operation?
5. Is the instrumentation adequate?
6. At night, is the headlight beam bright, and does it remain bright when the engine is idling?

The Honda four-cylinder 736 cc four-stroke engine delivers 67 hp at 8,000 rpm for a top speed of 125 mph. This machine is equipped with a five-speed transmission and weighs 480 pounds.
(*American Honda Motor Company*)

7. Are controls placed correctly, or are they difficult to operate?

If the machine checks out satisfactorily, the next consideration is whether or not the dealer and his shop meet the standards for proper maintenance. Since the dealer is the one who will service the motorcycle and provide parts and other assistance when necessary, his shop should be fairly near your home. A visit to the dealer will reveal the condition of his showroom and the shop or service area, and the manner in which his mechanics behave will reveal how efficiently the place is operated.

All dealers provide warranties on the motorcycles they sell, along with the required initial inspection and periodic servicing. An *Owner's Manual* and a *Parts Catalog* are also furnished the owner, and, if desired, a detailed *Shop Manual* at nominal cost. The dealer can also advise the

The famed Norton, with a two-cylinder 745 cc four-stroke engine, weighs only 409 pounds and provides top performance and riding comfort. Note upswept twin pipes. (Berliner Motor Corporation)

new rider about many things related to safe riding as well as how to protect his machine from theft.

With the popularity of minibikes and minicycles increasing, some exploratory comments are in order.

Generally a minibike carries no lights, while the minicycle is fully equipped for street riding, with lights, horn, and stoplight, and meets all licensing requirements.

Both types are mounted on small wheels, but the mini-

The Harley-Davidson is representative of the large, heavy American-made machines. This Sportster model is powered by a 883 cc two-cylinder V-type side-facing four-stroke engine. The larger Electra Glide model features a 1,200 cc engine. (*Harley-Davidson*)

The Moto-Guzzi features a two-cylinder V-type front-facing four-stroke engine of 757 cc which provides 60 hp. Two Dell'Orto carbs are used, and the rear wheel drive is by shaft. Top speed is appoximately 110 mph, in maximum comfort. (Berliner Motor Corporation)

cycle may have slightly larger wheels. The minicycle will feature a standard clutch and gearshift mechanism.

These machines range in weight from 70 to 130 pounds, with engines from 2 to 5 horsepower. Both types are excellent for basic riding instruction before graduating to standard-size motorcycles.

Index

Advanced spark, 27
Air and gasoline, 23, 24
Air filter, 35, 69
Alignment, wheel, 71
Alternator, 37
American motorcycles, 10, 11
Ammeter, 64
Ape hangers, 66, 73
Attitude, rider's, 73
Austin, W. W., 9
Automatic clutch, 15, 49, 67
Automatic oil feed, 31, 58
Automobiles, 64

Balance, 72
Basic preparation, 72
Basic rules, 76
Battery, 37, 64, 69, 87
  charge/discharge, 64
  and coil system, 36
  terminals, 38, 69
Bearings, 32, 57, 71
Bicycle, 9, 57, 72
Bottom dead center (BDC), 24
Bowl, carburetor, 34
Brakes, 50-52, 64, 67, 70, 73, 76
Breaker points, 37, 39, 69

Cams, 32
Carburetor, 34, 70, 76
Centrifugal-type clutch, 50
Chain, 21, 46-48, 70
Chain guard, 48
Charging battery, 38
Choke (air lever), 35, 76
Clerk, Sir Dugald, 29
Close ratio, 48
Clubs, 17
Clutch, 21, 42-44, 50, 76, 90
Clutch lever, 50, 66
Coast-to-coast records, 15
Combustion chamber, 22
Comfort, 53, 58
Competition, 7, 36, 58, 80, 82
Compression, 25, 28, 29, 39
Compression ratio, 25, 28
Condensation, 69
Condenser, 39, 69
Connecting rod, 21
Control cables, 69
Control levers, 62, 91
Cooling system, 40

Crankcase, 21, 32, 41, 68, 87, 89
Crankshaft, 39, 45
Crashbars, 60
Cylinder, 21

Daimler, Gottlieb, 9, 20
Damage, 68
Damper, steering, 55
Dangers, 73
Dealer, 91
Dipstick, 68
Directional signal lights, 64
Disc-type brakes, 52
Displacement (cc), 28, 81, 84
Double overhead cams (DOHC), 34
Down-shifting, 78
Dressing properly, 73
Drive chain, 70
Drive gear, 46
Drive shaft, 48
Driven gear, 46
Dry-type clutch, 44
Dynamo, 37

Electrolyte, 39, 69
Electric starter, 37
Electric switches, 62
Enduro bike, 82
Engine parts, 21
Engine rpm, 65
Engine startup, 75
Engine warmup, 76
Exhaust pipes, 41, 85, 89
Experimentation, 72
Eyeglasses, protective, 73

Fins, cooling, 41
Fenders, 58, 85, 87, 89
Four-stroke engine, 21, 24, 68, 70
Footpegs (footboards), 59, 89
Forks, 54
Frame, 9, 17, 39, 53, 85
Freeze up, 69
Fuel
  consumption, 85
  filter, 35, 69
  flow valve, 69, 76
  leakage, 69
  level, 76
  mixture, 21-24, 29, 30, 34, 39
  tank, 58, 76
Fumbling, 62

94

Gasket, 69
Gasoline engine, 9
Gearbox, 42
Gearing, 15, 29, 51, 85, 88
Gear ratio, 48, 82, 86
Gear shift lever, 50, 67
Gears, 21, 42, 45
Generator, 37
Ground, electrical, 39
Ground clearance, 86

Handlebar, 34, 50, 55, 64
Headlight, 64, 69, 87, 89
Heat, 32, 41, 71
Heavyweight machines, 80
Hedstrom, Oscar, 9
Hill climbing, 84
Helmet, 73
Horn, 64, 69, 87, 89
Horsepower, 20
Hubs, 55, 57, 71
Hydraulic brake system, 52

Ignition key, 39, 63, 76
  light, 64
  system, 35, 69
Illegal equipment, 73
Imported motorcycles, 12
Indian "Chief" and "Scout," 10
Indicators, 62
Input shaft, 46
Instruction, riding, 72
Insurance rates, 81

Jiffy stand (side stand), 59

Kick starter, 39, 71, 90
Kidney belts, 57

Lean mixture, 34
Leg guards, 60
License, rider's, 75
Lightweight machines, 80
Liska, Danny, 13
Lubrication, 32, 68, 71, 76

Maintenance, 68, 91
Magazines, monthly, 17
Magneto system, 36, 87
Manufacturer's instructions, 68
Mechanical faults, 73
Middleweight machines, 80
Minicycles, 15, 82, 88, 92
Minibikes, 49, 88, 92
Misadjustment, 68
Motocross (moto-cross, moto-x), 86
Mountings, engine, 54, 70

Neutral gear position light, 64, 76
Neutral position of gears, 42, 49
New rider, 72–79
Number of cylinders, 28, 34

Odometer, 64
Off-the-road riding, 88
Oil
  level, 68, 76
  pressure, 64
  pump, 30, 32
  tank, 58
Otto, August, 24
Otto cycle, 24
Output shaft, 46
Overhead cam type (OHC), 32
Overhead valve type (OHV), 32
Overheating, 69
Owner's Manual, 70

Paratroopers, 15
Parts, 91
Parts Catalog, 91
Performance, 20, 28, 47, 68, 81
Pipes, exhaust, 41, 85, 87
Piston, 21, 71
Piston strokes, 24, 29
Polarity, electrical, 39
Police, 74
Poor handling, 69, 71
Ports, 24, 29
Power, 15, 20, 28, 47, 51, 53, 88
Pressure, tire, 52, 58, 69
Primary chain, 46
Primer (tickler), 35, 76
Pushrods, 30

Racing, 10, 58, 86
Racks, 61
Rear brake pedal, 64
Registration, 75
Retarded spark, 28
Reverse gear, 49
Revolutions per minute (rpm), 65
Rear stop light, 52, 69
Rear wheel sprocket, 21, 48
Rearview mirror, 61
Rectifier, 37
Rich mixture, 34
Riding, 72
Rings, piston, 21
Road-holding, 57
Rockers, 30
Rotary disk, 29

Saddle (seat), 58
Saddlebags, 61

95

Sales brochures, 83
Scooter, 15, 17, 49
Secondary chain, 47
Scrambler, 82, 85, 87
Selecting a motorcycle, 80
Shaft drive, 48
Shields, leg, 41
Shifting up, 78
Shock absorbers, 57, 71
Shop Manual, 91
Signaling, 78
Skid plate, 41, 87, 89
Spark, 25, 36, 39, 69, 86
   arrestors, 41, 61
   plug, 24, 36, 39
Speed, 9, 51, 73, 74, 79, 84
Speedometer, 64, 71, 89
Spokes, 57
Sport cars, 64
Sprint bike, 86
Sprocket, rear wheel, 21, 47
Stability, 57
Stand, center, 59
Starting, 76
Steam engine, 9
Steering, 65, 71, 74, 77, 88
   head, 55
Stoplight, 52, 69
Street motorcycles, 80, 84
Suspension, 53–57, 85, 89
Swing arm, 48
Switches, 52, 62

Tachometer, 65
Technical knowledge, 73

Terrain, rough, 84, 89
Theft, 92
Throttle, 31, 34, 50, 66, 76
Thumper, 28
Tickler (primer), 35, 76
Timing, spark, 69
Tires, 20, 52, 57, 69, 86
Tools and toolbox, 58
Top dead center (TDC), 27
Torque, 21, 42, 46
Traffic
   conditions, 78
   safety, 78
Trail bike, 41, 61, 82, 88
Troubleshooting, 70, 75
Two-stroke engine, 21, 29, 58, 68

Vacuum, 24, 30
Valve gear, 24, 30, 32, 70
Valve springs, 34
Voltage regulator, 37

Warning, 78
Warranties, 91
Weight, 9, 20, 53, 72, 80, 93
Wet-type clutch, 44
Wheel alignment, 71
Wheelbase, 82
Wheel bearings, 70
Wheels, 20, 57, 92
Wide ratio, 48
Windshield, 61
Woods bike, 41, 61, 82
Workmanship, 90

The Author

CHARLES YERKOW has been the owner of three motorcycles at one time, has flown open-cockpit airplanes, and has taught judo. He has spent most of his waking hours at a typewriter. Mr. Yerkow, a born New Yorker, lives in Beechhurst, New York.

36902
c-1